Famous
Illustrated Tales of
SHRI KRISHNA

Famous Illustrated Tales of
SHRI KRISHNA

Published by

MAPLE PRESS PRIVATE LIMITED

Corporate & Editorial Office
A 63, Sector 58, Noida 201 301, U.P., India

phone: +91 120 455 3581, 455 3583
email: info@maplepress.co.in
website: www.maplepress.co.in

Reprinted in 2019

ISBN: 978-93-50339-13-8
Go to www.maplelibrary.com for more e-books

Printed at HT Media Ltd. Gr. Noida

10 9 8 7 6 5 4

Contents

Kansa–Devaki

A long time ago, Mathura, a city in Northern India, was ruled by King Ugrasen. He had a son named Kansa who was a great warrior and knowledgeable in scriptures, but over ambitious. He did not wait for his father to crown him. With the help of some demonic associates he dethroned his father, put him in prison and became the king. He had a sister named Devaki of whom he was extremely fond. When she got married to Prince Vasudeva; Kansa himself took to the reigns of the chariot to drop them to their palace.

On the way, a heavenly voice said to Kansa, "Oh fool! The eighth child of Devaki, whom you are taking with you, will kill you." On hearing these words Kansa immediately caught his sister by her hair and drew out his sword to kill her. Seeing this, Vasudeva tried to calm Kansa and spoke to him, "O Kansa! You are a great hero praised by all the warriors. How can you kill a woman and that too your newly married sister? This act will bring great disgrace and sin on you and your family. Please do not kill her. I promise to give all our children to you as soon as they are born."

Vasudeva was known for keeping his words and so Kansa left the thought of killing Devaki. Vasudeva was very happy and, praising Kansa, reached the palace. When the first child was born Vasudeva took him to

4

Kansa. Seeing the noble nature of Vasudeva, Kansa thought, "Why should I kill this child. The voice had said that only the eighth child of Devaki would kill me."

Suddenly Narada, a holy sage, appeared before Kansa and said, "Kansa all the Gods want to kill you. Please don't leave this child as it may harm you. Hearing these words Kansa got scared and snatching the baby from Vasudeva, flung it on a stone."

He then put Vasudeva and Devaki in the prison and killed the next five newborn children too one by one. When Devaki conceived her seventh child she hoped that the child would be saved from the cruel hands of Kansa. This time God Shesh, also known as Anant, had appeared in her womb himself. She was very scared as she knew Kansa would kill him too.

Seeing Devaki's condition, the heavenly Lord ordered Yoga Maya,

6

to help Devaki. He said, "O blessed Devi! Rohini, the elder wife of Vasudeva, lives in Gokul where Nanda is the prince and Yasodha is his wife. This place is not far from Mathura. Take the baby from Devaki's womb and place him in Rohini's womb. He will be born as the son of Devaki and called by the name Balarama. You must be born from the womb of Yasodha, the wife of Nanda." He also told Yoga Maya that she would be worshipped as Goddess Durga and in her other divine forms. Yoga Maya went to the earth and acted accordingly. Everyone thought that Devaki had a miscarriage and consoled her.

Kansa was very watchful when Devaki conceived for the eighth time as he knew that this child could be his killer. Kansa saw a divine splendour on Devaki's face, and thought, "The destroyer of my life has already entered her womb. What should I do now? I cannot kill my sister. He felt intense hatred for God and remembered him all the time. He kept Devaki and Vasudeva under close watch and gave strict instructions to the guards to inform him as soon as the child was born.

Krishna is Born

On the stroke of midnight, the eighth child of Devaki was born in a divine form. Vasudeva was the first to see this divinity. He said to the child, "We are blessed to have you, but I am very scared that Kansa and all others will know you if they see you in this divine form. Please transform yourself."

The Lord then assumed the form of a small and handsome baby through the power of his own *maya*.

He then said to Vasudeva, "If you are afraid of Kansa, immediately take me to Gokul and put me beside the sleeping Yasodha. Then bring here the baby girl Yoga Maya who is born to Yasodha." When Vasudeva stood up to take the baby, all the chains tying his body broke. The locked doors of the prison opened automatically and the sentries slept under the influence of Lord's *maya*. The dark passages of the prison were lit by a hallowed light. There was a gentle rain falling that night. Vasudeva carried the baby in a basket on his head and Shesh Naag, the residing serpent of the river, spread his hoods like an umbrella to ward off the rain. The deep Yamuna, which was flooded quietly calmed its waters and made way for Vasudeva.

Vasudeva crossed the Yamuna and reached Gokul easily. He was surprised to see everyone sleeping in the village.

Vasudeva placed the child near Yasodha and took away the baby girl sleeping beside her. He returned to the prison and placed the child near Devaki; then put chains around his ankles again. The prison doors closed on their own; and the sentries woke up hearing the baby crying. They ran and told Kansa of the birth of the child. Kansa jumped from his bed, and came to the prison where Devaki was confined. The helpless Devaki told Kansa, "O Kansa! Please do not kill this baby girl. You have already killed all my sons. Now only this girl is remaining. Please have pity."

Kansa did not listen to her crying, seized the baby girl and dashed her on a stone. The baby girl was no ordinary baby. She was a

Goddess. She slipped from his hands and appeared in the sky in her divine form with eight bejeweled hands holding weapons. She had a bow, arrow, shield, sword, conch, disc and a mace in her hands.

She said, "O fool! What will you get out of killing me? The one who will ultimately kill you has taken birth elsewhere. You are killing innocent children for no reason." Saying this she disappeared in the sky.

Kansa was struck with wonder when he heard these words. He released Devaki and Vasudeva and said, "Dear sister and brother-in-law, I am a great sinner. I have killed all your children. I am a wicked person and all my well wishers have left me. I do not know what fate awaits me in life and after death." He was filled with remorse and started crying.

Putana the Demoness

In Gokul, Yasodha believed that she had given birth to a boy and not a girl as she was unconscious at the time of the birth. As an heir was born to the Village Chief Nanda, there was a month long celebrations and rejoicing. There was an endless stream of *gopis* coming to pay their respects to Devaki, and they found the baby beautiful with his lotus eyes and ruby lips. Nanda gave presents to *brahmins* and organized a grand feast. People of Braj decorated their house and their cattles, and sang and danced with merriment.

In the meanwhile, Kansa called his counsellors and told them everything that Goddess Maya had spoken. The ministers said, "Do not worry O king, we will kill all the new born children found in towns or villages within a hundred kilometers radius. Kansa ordered the demons to create havoc in all places and return with news of the killings to his palace.

By Kansa's orders, the fierce demoness Putana went about killing children in towns, villages and pasture lands. Her only occupation was to kill babies. People hid their children in their homes in her fear. She had the power to fly and assume any form she liked.

One day this wanderer of the skies entered Gokul and assumed the form of a beautiful woman.

She entered the house of Nanda and saw the divine child sleeping in the cradle. Putana took the baby in her lap and told Yasodha, "What kind of mother are you? Can't you see the child is hungry? I am going to feed him with my milk." Putana looked so beautiful that Yasodha thought, "I am so lucky. My son is being fed by such a wonderful lady. I will not stop her." Putana took the child to another room. She had put a deadly poison on her breasts. The moment she put her breast in Shri Krishna's mouth to suckle, The Lord squeezed her breasts by both his hands and sucked her vital breath through them.

She screamed loudly, "Let go. Let go. No more!" Her eyes bulged out and she began sweating profusely. Then she started crying and throwing her hands and feet on the ground. Then she decided not to hide anymore and returned to her original form of the demoness. At once she fell dead like a dead log. When her giant body fell it crushed a large number of trees in the nearby area. Rohini and Yasodha came rushing to the spot on hearing the loud noise. They saw the baby playing fearlessly on the body of Putana. She was now free from her sins as she had suckled the Lord. The smoke that arose out of her burning body was fragrant, like that of sandal wood, as the touch of Shri Krishna's body had purified it! Putana became the foster mother of the Lord, even though she had harbored the evil intention of killing the child.

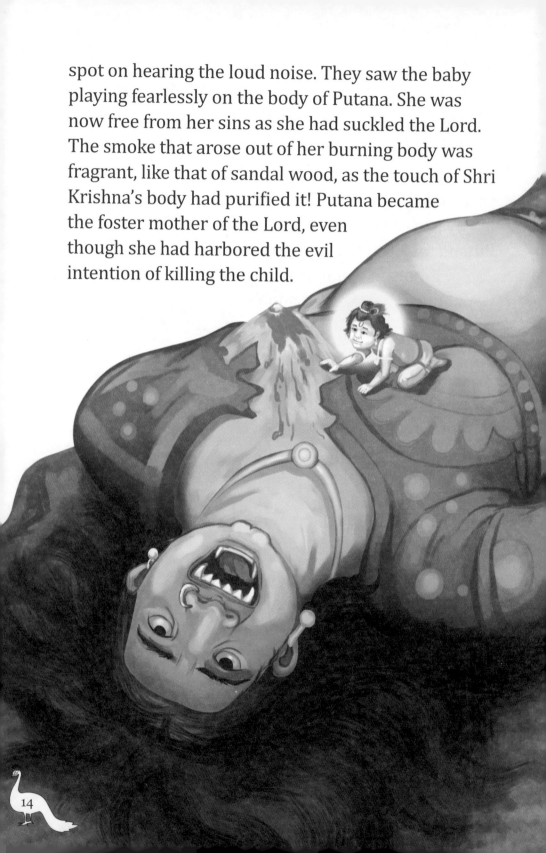

The Killing of Trinavarta

O ne day Yasodha was playing with little Krishna who was seated on her lap. Suddenly Shri Krishna became heavy as a mountain! Yasodha was not able to bear the weight of Krishna any more and so she made him sit on the ground. She then left him to attend to some household work.

A demon named Trinavarta, who was a servant of Kansa, had come to Gokul in the form of a hurricane. He carried away the child sitting on the ground with him. The whole of Gokul was covered

with dust and darkness for some time. No one was able to see anything for a few moments. Yasodha looked for her son in the storm but could not find him. She became lifeless with sorrow and fear and fell on the ground. When the effect of the storm became less, the *gopis* came rushing hearing Yasodha's cry.

The demon had flown with the child but was not able to go much further as Shri Krishna had become very heavy. He slowed down a bit. Immediately Krishna gripped his neck tightly and strangled him. The demon fell on the ground, with all his limbs shattered.

The *gopis* saw a giant falling from the sky. When they reached near that place, Shri Krishna was unhurt and happily playing on the chest of the dead *asura*. They were astonished and quickly took

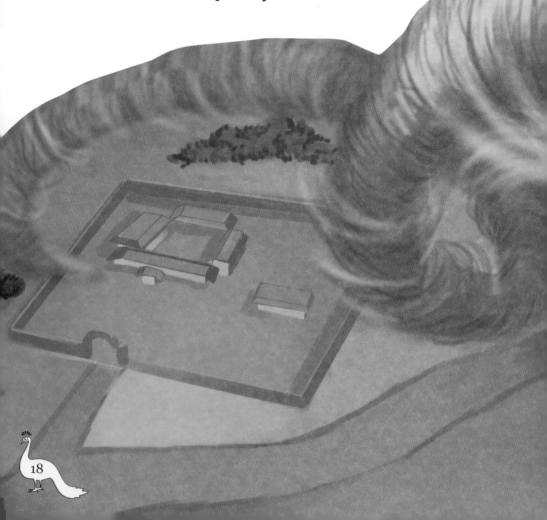

Shri Krishna to Yasodha. Yasodha and Nanda Baba felt that it was the result of their good actions that their son had come back unhurt. They felt blessed and prayed to God.

Krishna–The Naughty Boy

Young Krishna was very naughty. He would untie the cows and calves of the *gopis* when it was time for the milking. He would also steal the milk, butter and curd and share them with his friends. He would make holes in the pots hanging from the roped tripods, to find out their content. Then he would place a mortar below the pot and mount on it to reach them. He would illumine the dark room by the glitter of his own body and the jewels, to steal and then run away quickly.

Once a *gopi* was able to catch Krishna while he was stealing curd from her pot. She took him by the hand and went to inform his mother about his mischief. Krishna miraculously escaped from her hand. She found the missing child near his mother. She felt abashed and returned to her house.

One day Balarama and the other boys complained to Yasodha that Krishna had eaten mud.

Yasodha got afraid that this might affect Shri Krishna's health. She rebuked Krishna, "O my naughty child! Why did you eat mud?" Shri Krishna replied, "O mother! I did not eat mud. These boys have told a lie. You may examine my mouth." Yasodha said, "Open your mouth, my child!" When Krishna opened his mouth Yasodha was dazed to see the whole universe of animate and inanimate things, the sky, the mountains, continents, seas, the whole earth, air, fire, the sun, the moon and the stars, the seven islands, the planets, the mind, the senses, Vrindavan and herself in his mouth.

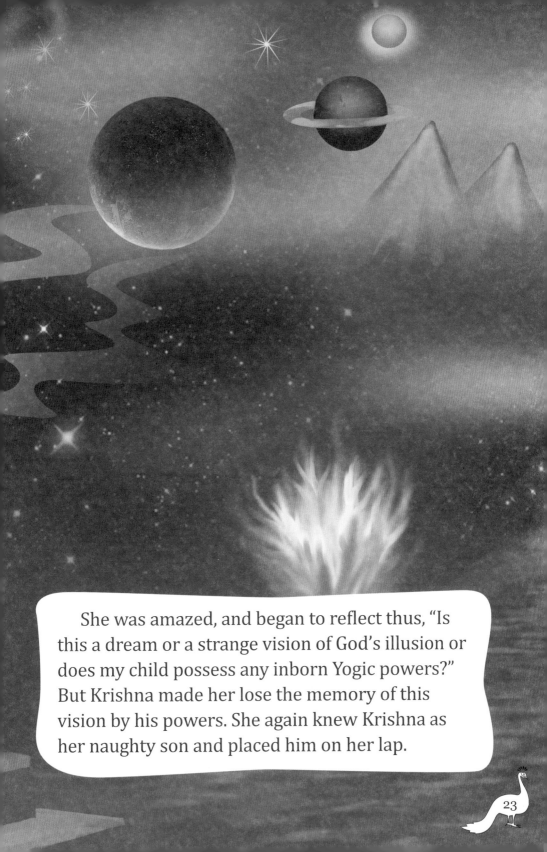

She was amazed, and began to reflect thus, "Is this a dream or a strange vision of God's illusion or does my child possess any inborn Yogic powers?" But Krishna made her lose the memory of this vision by his powers. She again knew Krishna as her naughty son and placed him on her lap.

Damodar: Tying of Krishna

One day Yasodha was churning butter for Krishna. She was so engrossed in her work that she did not realize that her little son had got up from sleep. He came to his mother as he was hungry and wanted his mother to feed him.

She placed him on her lap and suckled him. Suddenly she noticed that the milk that she had put on the stove was boiling and overflowing. She put Krishna down, leaving him still hungry, and went in a haste to remove the pot. Krishna became very angry. He bit his lips, broke the milk-pot with a stone, went to another room and started eating stale butter.

When Yasodha came back after a short while she found the pot of milk she was churning broken and the milk spread all over the floor. Yasodha at once guessed that it was her son's doing. Krishna had already left the place. She found Krishna standing on an overturned husking-stand distributing the contents of the hanging pots among the monkeys.

Yasodha quietly approached him with a stick. Krishna got down in haste from the husking-

stand and ran away. Yasodha ran after him and
caught him at last. She threw away the stick
and tried to tie him to the husking-stand with a
rope; but when she began to tie him the rope was
found to be short by a few inches.

   She brought another piece of rope and joined
it to the original one. When this also proved to be
short, she added another
piece. With every new
piece she added, the
rope was still short by
a few inches. She was
amazed at this! Krishna
saw that his mother was
thoroughly exhausted
by now and her body
was bathed in sweat.
He took pity on her and
allowed himself to be

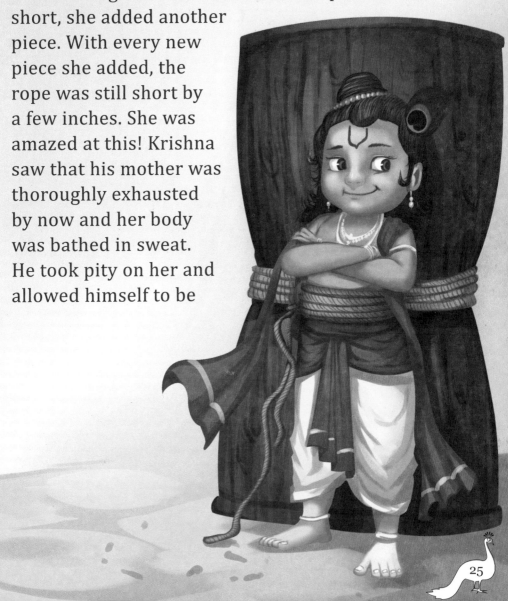

bound to the husking-stand. He was called Damodar after this incident as it means rope tied around the stomach.

27

Yamala Arjuna Trees

While being tied to the husking stand, Krishna started looking here and there and his eyes fell on two Arjuna trees. These Arjuna trees were sons of Lord Kubera in their previous life. Their names were Nala Kubera and Manigreeva. The two brothers joined a group of Lord Shiva's followers and became his devotees.

Slowly, they became very haughty as they had wealth and worshipped Lord Shiva. They thought they had become invincible. One day they took to drinking alcohol and frolicking with Gandharva girls in a river, in a naked state. Rishi Narada happened to pass that way. The celestial damsels felt ashamed at their nudity, and at once put on their clothes, as they were afraid of the curse by the *rishi*. But the two Yakshas who were under the influence of alcohol did not bother.

Hence Narada cursed them, "The sons of Kubera belong to a good family but have become insolent due to their wrong doings. Let them become trees. But, they shall not lose the memory of their birth as they are sons of my devotee Kubera. After one hundred Deva years, the touch of Shri Krishna shall save them." Thus the sons of Kubera became a pair of Arjuna trees in Vrindavan. They were known by the name Yamala Arjuna trees.

Shri Krishna approached the trees, drawing the husking-stand behind him and came between the trees. He then came out on the other side but the husking stand turned and got stuck between the trees. When Krishna pulled the stand by force the two trees shook and fell on the ground with a crash. Two handsome men came out of the trees and illuminated the place with their luster. They praised Lord Krishna and then rose up towards the heaven. Hearing the terrible noise, the *gopis* and village men came to the spot. They saw the two Arjuna trees on the ground. When Nanda Baba came to the spot the men told them what they had seen. They said,

"This is all Krishna's doing. He gave a pull and the two trees fell down with a crash. We also saw two persons coming out of the trees."

But no one could believe that such a small boy could uproot two big trees. They could see that Shri Krishna was still tied to the husking-stand. Nanda Baba untied the rope that bound Krishna and did not give much importance to the talk of the men.

Krishna in Vrindavan

Days passed. Krishna and Balarama enjoyed their childhood by playing with the other village boys. One day, while they were out on the street, an old woman came to sell fruits. She called out but no one purchased from her. She was very tired when Krishna noticed her and said, "Mother, give me some fruits."

The old lady immediately put her basket on the ground and filled Krishna's palms with fruits. In return she had to be paid some grains. Asking her to wait Krishna went in, filled his palms with grains and returned. But the grains fell from his hands and only few remained. Krishna placed those few grains in her basket. The old women smiled at his innocence and filled his palms with more of the choicest fruits. When she returned to her cottage and opened her basket she was surprised to see that the basket was filled with pearls and diamonds.

In spite of these miracles the elders of Gokul were getting worried. They thought that their village was becoming the target of evils spirits. First it was Putana, then the whirl wind and now uprooting of the trees. They decided to go to a safer place. They thought Vrindavan would be a safe place as its location was good. The river Yamuna was flowing near Vrindavan and

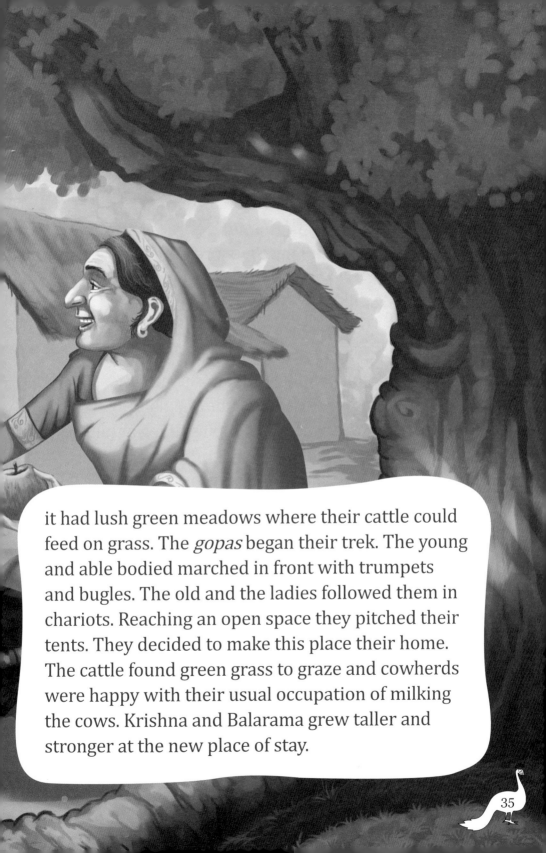

it had lush green meadows where their cattle could feed on grass. The *gopas* began their trek. The young and able bodied marched in front with trumpets and bugles. The old and the ladies followed them in chariots. Reaching an open space they pitched their tents. They decided to make this place their home. The cattle found green grass to graze and cowherds were happy with their usual occupation of milking the cows. Krishna and Balarama grew taller and stronger at the new place of stay.

Bakasur

Once Krishna, Balarama and their friends took their herds for grazing. They took lots of playing materials with them too. They played with other cowherd boys and simultaneously tended to the calves on the bank of the Yamuna. They played the flute and danced with joy. They pretended to be oxen and staged mock fights with each other. They enjoyed speaking like the peacock, koel and monkey. Suddenly a demon named Bakasur took the form of a calf and mixed among their herd. He had the evil intention of killing Krishna and Balarama. Krishna came to know of this and pointed him out to Balarama. Then he silently approached the demon smiling at him. He caught him by the hind legs and tail and whirled him around in the sky and threw him against a tree. The tree fell and the demon was killed. The cowherd boys could not believe that their little Krishna could do this. They praised Shri Krishna and shouted, "Nobody can harm us till Shri Krishna is with us."

One day the cowherd boys took their calves to the banks of a lake to drink water. They saw a huge mountain like monster sitting there. He was the another demon also named Bakasur who had taken the form of a large crane. His beak was very sharp. The demon crane suddenly pounced at Shri Krishna and lifted him with his beak and put him in his mouth. The *gopas* were so scared that some of them fainted. Krishna started to raise the temperature of his body and became so hot that the crane could not keep him in his mouth. Its mouth started burning and so he spit Shri Krishna out. Sometime later he tried to catch Krishna again with his hard beak. Shri Krishna held the two

beaks apart and tore them as a sugarcane is torn!
The demon Bakasur died. Everyone was happy and
heaved a sigh of relief. The Gods showered flowers
on Krishna. Krishna returned with all the *gopas* and
the cattle to his village.

Aghasura–the Deadly Serpent

One day Krishna was playing with the boys in the forest. At that time a mighty demon called Aghasura came. When he saw Shri Krishna playing and enjoying with his friends he became very angry. Aghasura was the brother of Putana and Bakasur and was sent by Kansa to kill Shri Krishna. He thought, "He has killed my brother and sister and continues his life playing happily! He deserves to be killed too. I will take my revenge now by killing Krishna along with Balarama and their friends."

The wicked demon took the form of a huge python. His body became so big that it looked like an enormous log. He sat down and opened his mouth very wide so he could swallow all the children. His mouth was so large that the lower lip touched the ground and the upper lip seemed to touch the sky. His mouth looked like a cave with sword like sharp teeth. There was darkness inside his mouth. His tongue was like a wide red road and his breath seemed like a raging storm. His eyes shone like fire.

When the boys saw him they thought it was a great big cave. All the boys clapped their hands in delight and entered the mouth of the demon with their cattle. All the while they talked and wondered if they were going to discover something nice inside the dark cave. They did not fear anything as they knew that Shri Krishna was with them and if something happened, he would be there to rescue them.

The demon did not close his mouth as he was waiting for Krishna to enter. Krishna, knowing very well that the *gopas* had entered the wicked Aghasura's mouth, followed his friends and went into his mouth. Aghasura then closed his mouth immediately. The boys were scared at this. Krishna calmed his friends

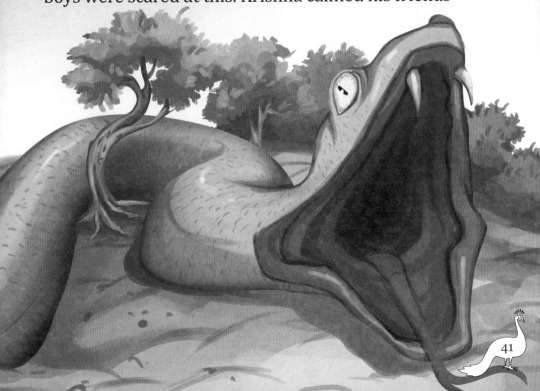

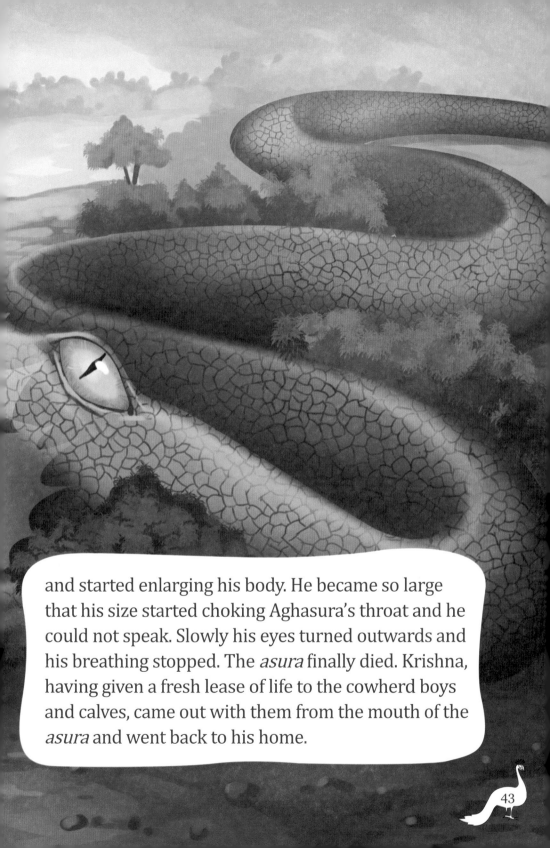

and started enlarging his body. He became so large that his size started choking Aghasura's throat and he could not speak. Slowly his eyes turned outwards and his breathing stopped. The *asura* finally died. Krishna, having given a fresh lease of life to the cowherd boys and calves, came out with them from the mouth of the *asura* and went back to his home.

Dhenukasur

One day Sridaman, the best friend of Balarama and Krishna, along with Subala, Stoka and other companions approached Krishna and Balarama and said, "Not far off from Vrindavan is a beautiful grove of palmy trees. The trees are full of ripe fruits. But nobody can enter it, because one *asura* named Dhenuka lives there with his family and prevents people from entering the grove. He has assumed the form of a donkey. He is so powerful that he can kill anyone who tries to enter the garden. He has already killed many men. Therefore people do not enter that place out of fear." They said, "We can smell the fragrance of the fruits even from here. They are very tempting. We want to taste them." Krishna and Balarama agreed to take them all there.

On reaching, Balarama boldly entered the forest and shook the trees violently. Numerous fruits fell down from the trees. When Dhenuka heard the sound of the falling fruits, he rushed forth and violently kicked Balarama on his chest with his hind feet. Balarama took hold of the donkey by both its hind feet

and whirled him. He then hurled it with all his force against a very large palm tree.

The *asura* died. All the kith and kin of Dhenuka attacked both Balarama and Krishna. They all were killed by Balarama and Krishna too in no time. The companions of Krishna and Balarama ate the fruits to their heart's content. After the death of Dhenuka and his family, other people started entering the grove fearlessly and the cattle also freely grazed on the pastures in that grove.

Lord Brahma-Krishna

Once Krishna took all his friends to the sandy bank of the river Yamuna. He told them, "Here the sand is soft and clean, we can all play here. But let us have some food first." They left their calves to graze and sat down to have their meal. While they were having fun eating and talking, their calves strayed deep into the jungle in search of grass.

When they looked for their herds later, they

could not find them. The cowherd boys were overtaken with fear. Krishna told them not to worry and said, "I will look for and bring back the calves." He took the last bites of food in his hand and went out in search of the calves. Lord Brahma was watching all this, and decided to test Krishna.

He took the calves and the cowherd boys to a secret place and quietly disappeared. Krishna could not find the calves in the forest, and when he returned to the sandy bank of the Yamuna he found that the cowherd boys were also not there. He sensed at once that Lord Brahma was playing a trick to test him. Krishna then himself assumed the form of the calves and the cowherds. He then returned to Vrindavan.

The mothers were happy to see their boys back home. Due to the divine powers of Lord Krishna, the mothers became more attached to their sons. The cows also began to show extraordinary love to their calves.

Krishna went on playing this game for almost a year. When only five or six days remained for the completion of the year, Balarama began to suspect something and reflected, "I have never witnessed such deep affection by the cows toward the calves that had been weaned long ago. The residents of Vraja are also showing more love and affection towards their sons. Surely

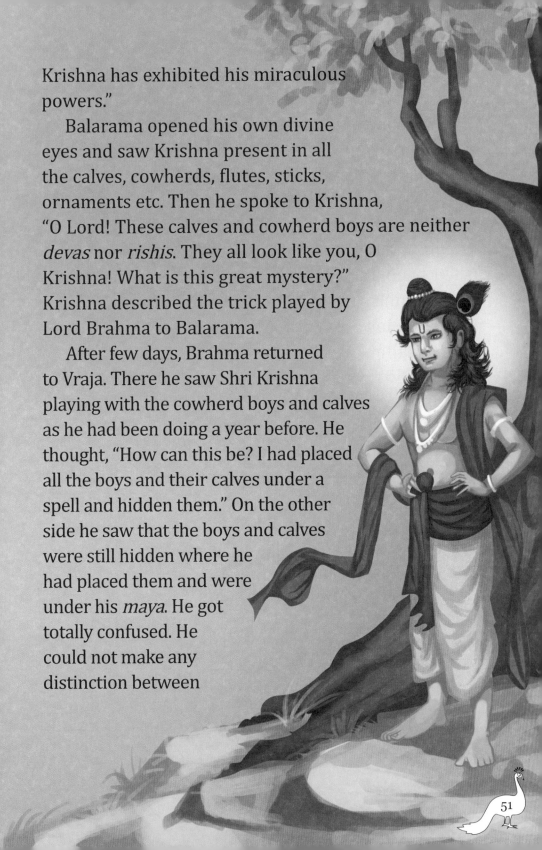

Krishna has exhibited his miraculous powers."

Balarama opened his own divine eyes and saw Krishna present in all the calves, cowherds, flutes, sticks, ornaments etc. Then he spoke to Krishna, "O Lord! These calves and cowherd boys are neither *devas* nor *rishis*. They all look like you, O Krishna! What is this great mystery?" Krishna described the trick played by Lord Brahma to Balarama.

After few days, Brahma returned to Vraja. There he saw Shri Krishna playing with the cowherd boys and calves as he had been doing a year before. He thought, "How can this be? I had placed all the boys and their calves under a spell and hidden them." On the other side he saw that the boys and calves were still hidden where he had placed them and were under his *maya*. He got totally confused. He could not make any distinction between those he placed under his own *maya* and those who were created by the *maya* of Krishna.

Brahma wanted to delude Krishna, but he himself became deluded. He then saw Shri Krishna present in all cowherd boys and calves. Each of the boys possessed Krishna's blue complexion and were clad in his yellow silken robes. All had four hands and the divine weapons. All wore crowns on their head, ear-rings, necklaces, bangles, trinkets and shining rings. He also saw many *brahmins* worshipping Shri Krishna. Seeing this wonderful sight Brahma was amazed and awestruck.

Shri Krishna then removed the veil of *maya*. Brahma came forward and prayed at the feet of Shri Krishna again and again with tears in his eyes and praises on his lips. Brahma then brought all the calves and cowherds back to the Yamuna bank. Shri Krishna took the calves and cowherd friends to their homes. Although one year had passed, but his friends thought it was only a moment since Krishna had left them!

Kaliya Serpent

A poisonous snake of gigantic size named Kaliya lived in a cavern at the bottom of river Yamuna. It had poisoned the water and the fish in the river were slowly dying. Even the Kadamba tress on the river bank died due to its poisonous effect. The cows drinking the river water would lie dead on the bank of the river.

Shri Krishna noticed that a venomous snake was making life difficult for the people of Vrindavan. He wanted to expel the serpent from the river in order to purify the water. Shri Krishna tightened his girdle, climbed a lofty Kadamba tree, and jumped into the middle of the river. The water sprayed and overflowed the banks. The serpent fiercely attacked Krishna and tightened him in its coil.

The cows and the *gopa* boys became scared for Krishna. When Nanda, Yasodha and other *gopas* came to the river, they saw him in the grasp of the powerful serpent and wept bitterly. Nanda wanted to jump in the river and save their son, but Balarama stopped him from doing so as he knew Shri Krishna was no ordinary boy. He was a God and would overpower the serpent. Shri Krishna, then shrunk himself and came out from the clutches of the serpent.

Kaliya tried to bite Krishna, but he put his foot on his hood, and danced upon his head. Kalia had one thousand hoods, and each hood had a red stone embedded in it. Shri Krishna trampled down with his feet on each of the hoods. The body of the serpent was thus shattered. The serpent sought the protection of the Lord. The wives of the serpent praised Krishna and prayed for their husband's life. The Lord stopped his dance and pardoned Kaliya.

Krishna said, "O serpent! Do not stay here anymore. Go to the sea immediately with all your kinsmen and, wives. Let the water of the Yamuna be used by the cows and men. I know that you left Ramanaka island for you feared Garuda and came to live in this pool. But now, as your hoods bear the marks of my feet, Garuda will not touch you." There upon Kaliya proceeded to the Ramanaka island in the sea with his wives, friends and children. The waters of the Yamuna then turned as sweet as nectar.

Kaliya started living on the island of Ramanaka with other serpents. They made offerings in the

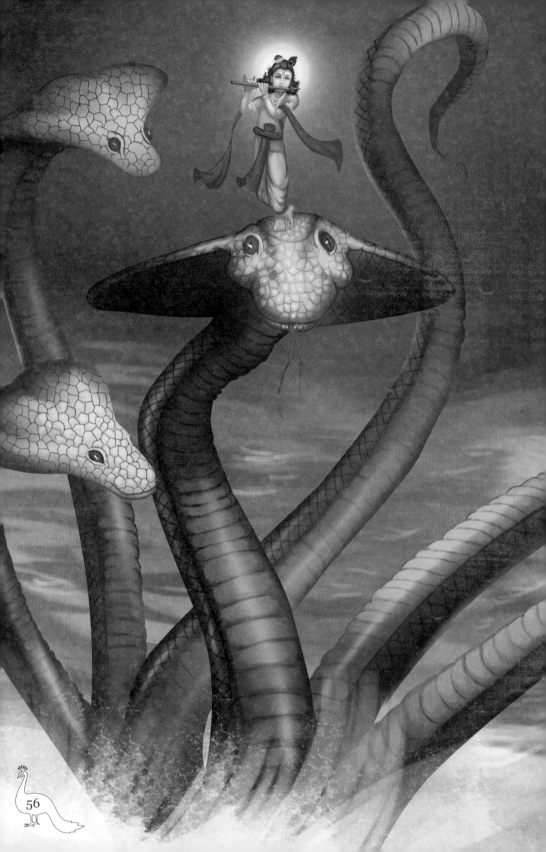

form of presents and sacrifices to Garuda (Lord Vishnu's carrier) who also lived on the same island. Everyone lived peacefully thereafter.

Govardhan puja and Lord Indra

One day, Krishna observed that the people of Vrindavan were preparing for the worship of Lord Indra. He asked his father Nanda, "Tell me, O father! What is this festive occasion? By whom and how is the sacrifice to be performed?"

Nanda replied, "My beloved child! Indra is the Lord of the clouds. He will give us rain if we worship him. The rains give life to all beings. The trees bear fruits and the grass grows green. Our cows graze happily and we live because of our cows. Therefore, people worship Indra by returning a portion of the harvest to him as sacrifice."

Krishna replied, "O father! "Our wealth and prosperity is due to our own actions. Where does Indra come in it? If at all we have to worship we should worship the hillock named Govardhan, which sustains us and our cattle."

Nanda and other *gopas* agreed to this and did as Krishna said. The *gopas* and *gopis* dressed in their best clothes and carrying vessels of milk and *ghee* and *curd* began to worship Govardhan. They made offerings to the cows, to the *brahmins* and to the hillock. Shri Krishna assumed another gigantic form and manifested himself on the top of the hill in order to confirm the faith of the *gopas*. He told the people that he was the deity presiding over the mountain. He then began to consume the offerings that were made to the hill.

Indra, the Lord of the heaven became very angry when he saw that the sacrifices meant for him were now being given to Govardhan. He wanted to teach the people of Vrindavan a lesson. He sent forth his clouds and winds. The thunder rolled and burst with a heavy downpour of rain. Continuous lights lit up the sky. Houses and haystacks started flying in the air. Hail stones

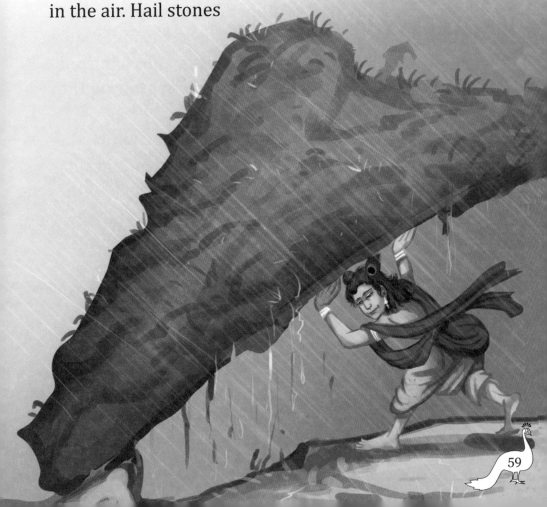

pelted without mercy. The people of Vrindavan cried, "Protect us O Krishna! We take refuge in you." Krishna said, "Do not be afraid. Enter this cave at the bottom of Govardhan with your flock." So saying this he lifted the mountain Govardhan with trees high above his head. The people of Vrindavan took shelter beneath the mountain. There was continuous rain for seven days. Shri Krishna held up the hill for seven days continuously without moving an inch. Indra was quite amazed. His pride was destroyed. He finally withdrew the clouds and winds.

The *gopas* went back to their homes with their cows. Shri Krishna set down the mountain in its original place. The *gopas* were struck with wonder. They came to Nanda and said, "This boy of seven years uprooted the Govardhan hill from the earth and held it up with one hand continuously for seven days. This marvelous feat cannot be done by an ordinary man. Your son is certainly the Lord of all Lords. He is the *atman* of all beings." Indra and Surabhi came down from heaven. Indra fell at the feet of Shri Krishna and begged forgiveness for his mistake.

Krishna in Mathura

Krishna and Balarama once decided to visit the city of Mathura. When they reached there, it was evening. Nanda Baba was waiting to receive them. Shri Krishna and Balarama had come with Akura who had brought them both in his chariot. When they asked him to go home and take some rest, Akura said he did not want to leave them and requested them to come to his home too.

But Shri Krishna said, "Not today Akura, we have to kill Kansa first and then we shall be able to enjoy your hospitality." Akura gave the message of their arrival to Kansa and went home.

The next day Krishna and Balarama set out with their friends to see the city of Mathura. The city was very beautiful. The houses had big doors made of gold and silver. They were beautifully decorated. There were gardens and well paved streets. The balconies and floors were studded with jewels. There were beautiful flowers in the gardens and on the streets and footpaths. The city showed grandeur. They saw ladies crowded on terraces and windows showering flowers on their arrival.

As they moved into a street, they saw a washerman approaching with his attendants carrying bundles of dyed clothes. Krishna called

63

out, "Can you give us some clothes? We will reward you." The washerman spoke to them very rudely, "You are not worthy of these. These clothes are for our King Kansa. You will be killed so just run away."

On hearing these words, Krishna extended his arm and knocked his head off. The attendants ran away in fear leaving the bundles on the ground. Krishna and his friends untied the bundles, took out the beautiful and costly clothes and wore one each. Shri Krishna chose a gold coloured garment and Balarama a blue one. A tailor in the city was very happy to alter the garments to their sizes immediately. He was suitably rewarded for helping Shri Krishna and his friends.

They moved ahead in the new attire and met a garland maker on another street. He was very happy to see Shri Krishna and Balarama and placed his basket of garlands in front of them. Krishna chose Vaijayanthimala and Balarama chose a garland of blue lotuses. The garland maker was given the boon of good health and life long prosperity in return.

They continued their journey in the town like conquerors. They saw a woman who had a beautiful face but was bent on three sides in her body. She was limping. Shri Krishna said, "O beautiful lady, who are you and for whom are you carrying the sandalwood in your hand? If you give us this sweet smelling scent we will reward you." The woman looked at Shri Krishna and said, "O beautiful, I am carrying this sandalwood and other scents for Kansa but you both are more deserving. I shall give them to you." Krishna was very happy with her affection and devotion. He decided to remove her bends and make her stand straight. So he pressed his toes on her feet and lifted her chin with his two fingers. At once her whole body straightened and she became a truly beautiful woman. She was very happy and pleaded them to stop at her home. Shri Krishna said, "We have other works to complete, but we will come on our way back." Then he left her and walked further with his friends.

Killing of Kansa

Krishna and his friends reached the place where the Dhanur Yagna or the worship of the bow was being performed. Kansa had kept the great bow of Lord Shiva in a hall for public worship. Each person performed some rituals around the bow and prayed with folded hands. Krishna inched forward, lifted the mighty bow and pulled on the string. The string broke in two with a loud noise. The soldiers who were guarding the bow rushed with their weapons towards Shri Krishna. But Krishna and his friends easily beat them up. The soldiers wanted to tie them but they escaped easily. They left the place and walked on to see more of the city.

Next morning, Kansa announced a wrestling march. Citizens were invited and were seated in the galleries in the arena. Kansa took his seat at the highest place. The drums started to beat. The mighty wrestlers Kansa Chanur, Mushtik, and others were already inside the wrestling ground. When Shri Krishna and Balarama approached the entrance of the arena, they found a huge elephant named

Kuvalyapeedha, along with his caretaker mahout, blocking their way. They requested the mahout to give way, but he did not agree. The mahout was very angry and urged the tusker to kill Shri Krishna. Krishna was ready and he promptly stepped aside. The elephant immediately turned around and took Krishna on his trunk.

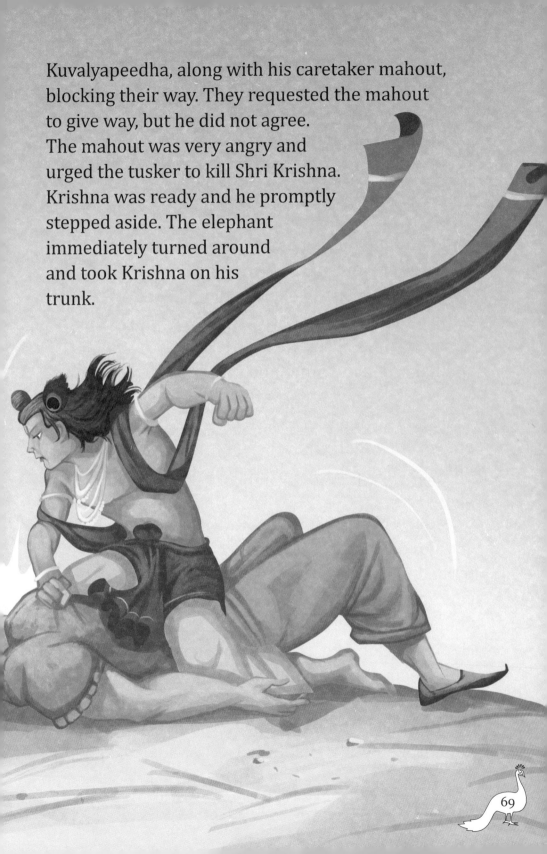

Shri Krishna easily slipped down and placed himself under his belly and caught hold of his tail. He started pulling the tail and dragging the elephant as a playful child drags a calf for fun. Then he ran in front of the elephant and pretended to fall on the ground. The elephant, which was running after Krishna, pierced the ground with his tusks to kill him, but could not pull out his tusks. Shri Krishna was quicker than him and had already taken his trunk in his hand. He gave the elephant a mighty blow. The elephant fell down dead. Krishna then pulled out the blood dripping tusks. Krishna shouldered one tusk and Balarama the other and thus armed, they both entered in the wrestling arena.

People sitting there were delighted to see such brave young men and prayed for their well being. Chanura and Mushtika were waiting for them. Chanura said, "We have heard that you are good wrestlers. Let us please the King Kansa as he is very fond of the wresting sport." Krishna teasingly replied, "Chanura we are too young to fight with you. You must fight with people of your age." Chanura retorted, "Have you not just killed a mighty elephant? Don't be a coward and let us fight." The fight began. Chanura fought with Krishna and Mushtika with Balarama.

The ladies who had come to watch the wrestling fainted seeing this unfair match. Vasudeva and

Devaki who were also present could not bear to see their children fighting with the professional wrestlers. Suddenly they saw that Krishna and Balarama had laid their opponent on the ground and were on the top of them fisting very fiercely. Chanura and Mushtika could not take the powerful blows. They began to vomit blood and died. Two of their brothers came in to fight but Shri Krishna and Balarama killed them too. There was a happy uproar in the stands. Shri Krishna brought all his friends inside the arena and they all danced and sang in victory. Kansa was very angry. He stopped the playing of the drums and asked his soldiers to kill Vasudeva and Devaki.

He was screaming, "Bind them all, kill them all." Shri Krishna immediately jumped and reached the stage where Kansa was sitting. Kansa took out his sword to kill Krishna, but Krishna was on top of him and threw him down. As he lay on the ground, Krishna stood on him with his entire weight. As Kansa was dying Krishna took on his divine form. The onlookers saw a wonderful spectacle. A glorious luster emerged from the body of Kansa and entered Shri Krishna. Kansa had attained salvation. Krishna and Balarama then left for the *ashram* of Sage Sandipini for their formal education.

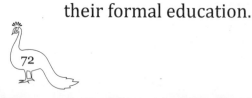